CORNISH CAROLS
FROM
AUSTRALIA

A new edition of *The Christmas Welcome,* compiled — with an introduction — by

Philip Payton BSc PhD

TRURAN

First published in 1984
By Dyllansow Truran
Trewolsta, Trewirgie, Kernow, [Cornwall]

Printed in Great Britain
by Penryn Litho, Mabe, Penryn, Kernow

ISBN 0 907566 92 8

Acknowledgements

This work is principally not my own but that of the nineteenth-century Cornish composers who wrote the Cornish Carols, and it is to them that the greatest acknowledgement is due — not only for this book, but for their immeasurable contribution to the Cornish cultural heritage. Alas, little is known today of these composers, and so the greatest difficulty has been experienced in tracing the holders of any remaining copyrights. However, the publisher and author should be delighted to include appropriate acknowledgements in subsequent editions, and request that any copyright holders contact Dyllansow Truran directly.

Acknowledgement is due also to Rigby Publishers for permission to reproduce cartoons from Oswald Pryor's *Australia's Little Cornwall* and *Cornish Pasty*. The author wishes to thank, too, the Barr Smith Library for their co-operation and for allowing access to the now extremely rare original *The Christmas Welcome*. Similar thanks go to the Newspaper and Archives sections of the State Library of South Australia, especially for allowing access to D5133 (Misc.) *Musical Scores of hymn tunes by James Richards*.

Finally, the author is indebted to Mrs May Cocks for permission to inspect the Minutes of the Cornish Association of South Australia.

Philip Payton

Cover cartoon by Oswald Pryor

Introduction

Hidden away on a stack shelf in the Special Collections of the Barr Smith Library at the University of Adelaide is a slightly tattered, rather slim volume — its pages yellowing with the passage of time — entitled *The Christmas Welcome: A Choice Collection of Cornish Carols*. Its modest, even scruffy appearance and its prosaic title belie its true worth, however, for (although other copies of the work **may** have survived elsewhere) this little booklet is extremely rare — if not unique. First published circa 1893, in the copper-mining town of Moonta in South Australia, *The Christmas Welcome* can never have run to more than a few hundred copies and it is sheer chance that one has survived intact to find its way into the University Library. There it has lain for some years, examined occasionally by research students (of which the present author was one in the mid 1970s) but generating little interest or excitement. Until now, that is!

In Cornwall, enthusiasm for the traditional Cornish Carols has never really waned since their nineteenth-century heyday, but in recent years there has been an upsurge in both popular and academic interest in the subject. This was reflected first of all in Inglis Gundry's *Now Carol We*, published in 1966, which was followed by the *Strike Sound!* collection of Padstow Carols. More recently still, Kenneth Pelmear's delightful *Carols of Cornwall* and Leonard Truran's *Thomas Merritt: Twelve Cornish Carols* have appeared on the scene, attesting to the continuing and growing demand for the music and words of the Cornish Carols to be made more generally available. With this demand in mind, it was felt that a new edition of *The Christmas Welcome*, with an especially written introduction setting the Carols in their historical context, would be much appreciated by both the Cornish and South Australian publics. Hence this present volume, which the author has reluctantly renamed *Cornish Carols From Australia* to give an unambiguous indication of its origin.

Christianity in Cornwall has always possessed a peculiarly "Cornish" stamp, from the earliest days of the Celtic Saints — whose names survive in Church dedications throughout the land — to the modernity of Cornish Methodism. And Cornish Carols are part of this singular tradition, as purely Cornish as the Medieval Miracle Plays in the Cornish language, their popularity in the last century mirroring the rise of the Methodist movement. These Carols had their roots, argues Kenneth Pelmear, in the western mining parish of Illogan, but from there they spread throughout Cornwall — to Redruth, St. Day, Padstow, Morwenstow and Stratton, to name some of the more famous "homes" of the Cornish Carol. As early as 1833 some Cornish Carols were included in a general collection of Christmas Carols published by William Sandys, but the great era of the Carol in Cornwall was from 1850 until 1900. Old words and tunes were set down on manuscript, often for the first time, while new composers arose to write new Carols — or to set existing Methodist hymns to new tunes. A distinctly Cornish form emerged, Pelmear noting that "A florid air, frequent word repetitions and a large flowing bass were the chief characteristics of this form of carol."

Thomas Broad and J. Coad, both from Illogan, were responsible for developing this style and they were followed by many others — most of whom were simple miners, fishermen or agricultural labourers — who perpetuated the Carol tradition throughout the last century. Well-known composers included W.B. Ninnis of Helston, Colan Williams of St. Ives and Wilson Manhire of Bugle, while in the period 1890 to 1925 several local collections of Carols — such as those of Polperro, Redruth and Penzance — were actually published. The epitome of the nineteenth-century Cornish Carol composer, however, was Thomas Merritt. The son of an Illogan miner, he was born in 1863 and as a youth worked as a mine labourer at Carn Brea and Tolvaddon. Ill-health forced him to abandon this occupation and thereafter he earned a modest living as music teacher. His Carols were perhaps his finest achievements, but he also wrote several works for the Cornish brass and silver bands, including a march for the Coronation of Edward VII in 1902. He died in 1908 at the relatively young age of 46.

The period 1850 to 1900, the great age of the Cornish Carol, was also the era of the "Great Migration" — when literally thousands of Cornish men and women left their homeland to travel to the ends of the earth, to Australia, North and South America, South Africa and countless other countries. The dreadful "Hungry Forties" precipitated the first major exodus and thereafter the declining fortunes of the mining industry (the crash of Cornish copper in the 1860s, the tin crisis in the 1870s) combined with other problems (the agricultural depression of the 1870s, the gradual decline of fishing) to perpetuate the Cornish emigration. Gold Rushes and other mineral bonanzas in far-off lands beckoned enticingly to the unfortunate in Cornwall.

The Province of South Australia was proclaimed in December 1836 and, paradoxically, although it was the last Australian colony to be settled, it was nevertheless the first to develop its mineral wealth. Consequently, as detailed in the author's *The Cornish Miner in Australia*, South Australia became a principal destination for emigrant Cornishmen and their families, the flow of Cornish miners — or "Cousin Jacks" as they were known — to the colony remaining strong until the end of the assisted passage scheme in 1886. Following the discovery of silver-lead deposits in the Adelaide Hills by two of these Cousin Jacks (their names were Thomas and Hutchins), Australia's very first metal mine — Wheal Gawler — was opened in 1841. Two years later came Australia's first discovery of copper, at Kapunda — an isolated spot some fifty miles north of the colonial capital of Adelaide. In 1845 there was a second major copper find, at Burra Burra — 100 miles north of Adelaide in what was then wild outback country. Cornishmen flocked to Kapunda and Burra Burra and around the two mines grew Cornish communities which preserved the traditions of the Old Country and became in every sense of the phrase "Little Cornwalls".

In 1851 gold was discovered in the neighbouring colony of Victoria and many Cousin Jacks abandoned Kapunda and Burra Burra to try their luck at the Rush, while at home in Cornwall attention switched abruptly from South Australia to the Goldfields. But in 1859 came a third, and even greater, discovery of copper, at Wallaroo on South Australia's Yorke Peninsula. Copper was also found at neighbouring Moonta in 1861 and hundreds of Cornish families — from Kapunda and Burra Burra, from the Victorian Goldfields and of course from Cornwall itself — moved to the new settlements on northern Yorke Peninsula. As before, the communities thus created were distinctly Cornish in character, the district centred on the townships of Wallaroo, Moonta and Kadina soon earning the nickname "Australia's Little Cornwall". Cornish customs, from wrestling to Midsummer Bonfires, thrived on Yorke Peninsula — and two elements of the Cornish inheritance which took especially strong root were Methodism and the making of music. And Cornish Carols, of course, were a meeting point for these two strands of the Cornish identity.

Cornish folk migrating to South Australia took their Carols with them, but — as in Cornwall — there emerged in the second half of the last century, amongst the Australian Cornish, a number of remarkably talented Carol composers. Thus *The Christmas Welcome*, which Oswald Pryor suggests was published in 1893 (although it may have been compiled at a rather earlier date), included several Carols which were old favourites from Cornwall. But the main body of the work, though still very much in the Cornish tradition, was actually written by Cornish composers in South Australia. Fortunately, their names have survived, recorded above each of the scores. They are, of course, all recognisably Cornish — J.H. Thomas, William Holman, Joseph Richards, J. Coad, John Hodge, James Richards, Thomas Spargo, William Andrew and Joseph Glasson. No doubt obituaries of most of these worthies lie hidden in the backnumbers of the various South Australian Methodist journals, if only one had the time and means to search for them, but few easily accessible biographical details have survived. Who, for example, was J. Coad? Is he the famous J. Coad of Illogan; if so, did he too migrate to South Australia, or were the Moonta people merely acknowledging his central role in the Carol tradition when they included an example of his work in their collection? But Coad is a common enough Cornish name; there must have been any number of J. Coads scattered across the world.

There are two composers we do know a little about, largely through the efforts of the late Oswald Pryor. In his splendid local history, *Australia's Little Cornwall*, Pryor dealt briefly with the Carol tradition and highlighted J.H. "Johnnie" Thomas and James "Fiddler Jim" Richards as Yorke Peninsula's principal composers. Pryor, of course, was a great cartoonist. And in his *Australia's Little Cornwall* appears a delightful characature of "Johnnie" Thomas, depicting him as a sprightly, impish little man, brimming over with enthusiasm and energy. Pryor's cartoons had a reputation for being extraordinarily true-to-life, his sketches capturing not only the physical characteristics but the personality as well. We can be fairly confident, therefore, that his drawing of "Johnnie" Thomas is an accurate likeness of the man.

1) Oswald Pryor's sketch of J.H. "Johnnie" Thomas. Pryor suggests that it was Thomas who edited the collection of Cornish Carols that was to become Grummet's *The Christmas Welcome*. "Cipher" was the pen-name used by Pryor in his early years as a cartoonist — for many years "Cipher" contributed on a regular basis to the Sydney *Bulletin,* his first appearance in that magazine being on 25th January 1912. His first-ever published cartoon appeared in the Adelaide *Quiz and the Lantern* on 9th October 1901.

"Fiddler Jim" Richards was clearly a musician of considerable ability. He was born at Perranporth in 1828 and emigrated to South Australia circa 1857. He made his way to the Burra Burra copper mine to find work as a miner and there joined the Primitive Methodist chapel. Following the new copper discoveries at Wallaroo and Moonta, he moved on to Yorke Peninsula and there became conductor of the Primitive Methodist choir. There he earned his reputation as an accomplished composer of Carols and hymn tunes. Surprisingly, only one of his compositions appears in *The Christmas Welcome*, though his name "Jas Richards" appears in bold print upon the cover of the original volume. It may be, however, that "Jos Richards" — to whom a number of the Carols are attributed — is merely an accidental mispelling of his name. Certainly, his works were popular throughout South Australia's Cornish community, his best-known tunes being "Rapture", "Dismissal" and "Everlasting Rest". Without fear of over exaggeration, one could venture to suggest that James Richards and "Johnnie" Thomas together were Australia's answer to Cornwall's Thomas Merritt.

"C'mon, boays; double f's, guv-un-guts."

2) "C'mon, boays; double f's, guv-un-guts" — Pryor's impression of a Cornish choir in full voice. The choirs loved their Carols, but there was also a number of Methodist hymns that the Cornish foremost liked to claim as their "own". First and of these was "Lead, kindly, Light", always a firm favourite with the Cornish overseas — its words curiously appropriate for a mining people so far from home:

Lead, kindly Light, amid the encircling gloom,
Lead Thou me on;
The night is dark, and I am far from home;
Lead Thou me on.
Keep thou my feet; I do not ask to see
The distant scene — one step enough for me.

Looking a little more closely at *The Christmas Welcome* itself, it is interesting that the very first Carol in the collection is "Sound, sound your Instruments of joy" — one of Cornwall's favourite Carols. Coincidently, the same Carol is the first to appear in Pelmear's modern collection. In the latter, though, the tune is a well-known composition by W.B. Ninnis, while the Australian version is an arrangement by J.H. "Johnnie" Thomas. Thomas' words also differ in places from those of Ninnis, the Cornish form having five lines per verse while the Australian has only four. Of the other Carols, "What heav'nly music's this I hear", the tune this time by William Holman, is also well-known in Cornwall and is a Carol that seems always to have been popular with Cornish communities overseas. "Hail ever hail, The auspicious morn", by Joseph (James?) Richards, is a title reminiscent of Thomas Merritt's "Hail, Sacred Day, Auspicious Morn", though in other respects the Carols are quite different. William Holman's "Awake with joyful Strains of Mirth" is a version of Thomas Merritt's much-loved Carol of the same name. The remaining Carols in the collection are, apparently, of purely local (ie Yorke Peninsula) composition — but exhibiting the unmistakeable Cornish form.

The publication of *The Christmas Welcome* circa 1893 by A. Grummet, the local bookseller and stationer at Moonta, was perhaps prompted by the appearance — at about the same time — of local collections published in Cornwall. But clearly the Carol tradition was widespread on the Peninsula long before that date and, despite the inverted Antipodean seasons, Christmas remained — along with Whitsuntide, the Duke of Cornwall's birthday and Midsummer Eve — one of the miners' principal festivities. In December 1873 the *Yorke's Peninsula Advertiser* newspaper commented that, "To say that the miners' cottages were profusely decked with evergreens would be almost superfluous, for it is well known that Cornishmen, wherever they may be, delight in keeping up the good old custom of decorating their habitations at this season of the year ..." Later, in the 1890s, the Cornish miners from Yorke Peninsula took their Carols with them to Western Australia, when many Cousin Jacks joined the Goldrush to Kalgoorlie and Coolgardie. There, in a little shanty town known as "Moonta Camp", they organised a choir and at Christmas could be heard singing their traditional Cornish Carols.

Later still, in the early years of this century, Carols were still popular on Yorke Peninsula. The *People's Weekly* newspaper, published at Moonta, noted in its edition for 20 December 1902 that a special service "... consisting of Cornish carols ..." had been held in the East Moonta South Methodist chapel. In the following year the same newspaper again noted the performance of "... carols and Cornish recitations ...", while in December 1909 a large crowd assembled at the agricultural community of Agery (near Moonta) to sing "... the good old Cornish carols". In the December 1910 issue of the *Australian Christian Commonwealth* magazine, published in Adelaide, appeared S. Trevena Jackson's article, "The Cornish Xmas", in which he painted a cosy picture of the Cousin Jacks preparing for Christmas — the miners practising their Carols, the mothers baking saffron cake, and the boys and girls decorating the snug, Cornish cottages.

"*Lizbeth Jane's solo was lovely. Oo do she git 'er voice from?*"
"*From Granfer, of coorse. 'E used to play bass viol in Camborne choir.*"

3) "Lizbeth Jane's solo ..." — Pryor's brand of humour was instantly recognisable to anyone familiar with Cornwall and the Cornish. In 1950 A.L. Rowse wrote to Pryor that "It is extraordinary how true to type your Cornish characters are ...", Claude Berry adding in the same year that "It is extraordinarily refreshing, you know, for us stay-at-home Cornish folk to realise that thousands of miles across the ocean there are Cornish communities who share to the full our love of Cornwall and Cornish traditions and the Cornish humour ..."

After more than sixty years operation, the Yorke Peninsula mines of Moonta and Wallaroo were abandoned in 1923 — the victims of low copper prices and soaring costs — and thereafter, as many locals moved away to find work elsewhere, the district suffered a continuing dimunition of its Cornish identity. But the Carol tradition did not disappear overnight. Many of the unemployed miners headed for Adelaide, in the hope that they might find work in the capital, and there created some comment by forming themselves into choirs to sing the Cornish hymns and Carols. As late as 1931 there was still a "Moonta Harmony Choir", specialising in the singing of Cornish Carols, and the Minutes of the Cornish Association of South Australia for October 1933 note the existence of both a "Moonta Carol Party" and a "Kadina Carol Party". By July 1935, however, the *People's Weekly* was bemoaning the fact that the Carols were gradually falling into disuse. In more recent times, with the advent of the bi-annual "Kernewek Lowender" festival on Yorke Peninsula, interest in things Cornish — including the Carols — has increased dramatically, and, it is to be hoped, this volume will help to foster a particular interest in the district's Carol tradition.

The Carols were, of course, but one part of the Peninsula's Cornish musical inheritance. Moonta, Wallaroo and Kadina sported a bewildering number of brass and silver bands which, like the Carols, were connected intimately with the activities of the various Methodist chapels. There was "Bargwanna's Band", founded at Moonta in the early '60s, the "Moonta Mine Band", "Mr Ricard's Kadina Brass Band", "Tregonning's Cross Roads Fife and Drum Band", the "Copper City Brass Band", the "Wallaroo Mines Federal Band", with many more besides, but the most famous was the "Wallaroo Town Band". Founded in 1895 and nurtured in its early years by two exceedingly talented local musicians, Henry May (from Perranporth) and Arthur Chynoweth, it has survived to the present day (as the Kadina and Wallaroo Band).

4) Kadina's "Copper City Brass Band" in 1909, typical of the many such bands that once flourished on South Australia's Yorke Peninsula.

A further musical aspect of Methodist activity was the sacred music associated with funerals. Funerals on Yorke Peninsula tended to be elaborate affairs — impressively solemn, moving occasions, attended by large numbers of mourners and conducted with a simple but genuine dignity. Geoffrey Blainey suggests that the well-known Cornish "burying tune" — "Sing From the Chamber to the Grave" — was sung at such times, but certainly more popular were the works of James "Fiddler Jim" Richards. His "Rapture" was a firm favourite for funerals, set to the words of the hymn "Thee We Adore". A ritual developed whereby the coffin was picked up by the bearers during two lines from the third stanza of the hymn — "What e'er we do, where'er we be, We are travelling to the grave" — with the dirge-like strains of the tune drifting across the mineral leases. The Rev. William Francis James, who was born in Truro in 1846 and ordained as a Bible Christian Minister in 1872, emigrated to South Australia in 1884 in response to an urgent appeal for Methodist Missionaries for the colony. Writing in the *Burra Record* newspaper in 1902, he had this to say of Cornish funerals:

> Chacewater funerals were largely attended and the singing was memorable. Never shall I forget the sight of a funeral procession turning the corner of the street leading to the churchyard. The corpse was preceded by some twenty to thirty men, having good voices, with measured step and slow, singing a hymn to an appropriate tune. I have never heard anything like it, save at Moonta.

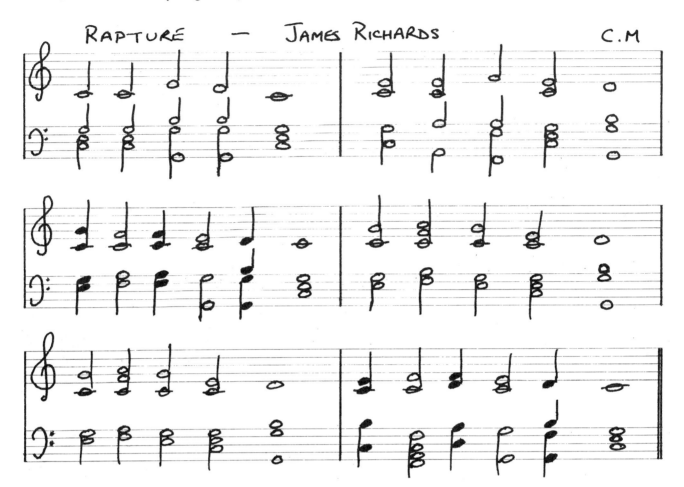

5) The musical score of "Rapture", James "Fiddler Jim" Richard's best-known and best-loved composition, a tune set often to Dr Isaac Watt's funeral hymn "Thee we adore":

> **Thee we adore, eternal Name!**
> **And humbly own to Thee**
> **How feeble is our mortal frame,**
> **What dying worms we be.**
>
> **Our wasting lives grow shorter still,**
> **As days and months increase;**
> **And every beating pulse we tell**
> **Leaves but the number less.**
>
> **The year rolls round, and steals away**
> **The breath that first it gave;**
> **Whate'er we do, where'er we be,**
> **We are travelling to the grave.**

The quality and skill of the singers, especially the male voice chapel choirs, was commented on by several writers and it is clear that the high standard of composition was matched by an equally impressive standard of performance. Secular tunes — especially "Trelawny", "The Song of the Western Men" — were always popular with the choirs, but it was the religious music that commanded their greatest attention and respect. One vocalist of particular note was Lesley Davey, the founding member of the Moonta Mines Male Voice Choir. In October 1907, according to an enthusiastic report in the *People's Weekly*, the crowds thronged to the East Moonta Literary Society's meeting to hear Lesley Davey sing "Lead, Kindly Light" — a tune which, as the late A.K. Hamilton Jenkin wrote, was for a time virtually the Cornish national anthem. There were, too, female vocalists of repute — the most successful being Jennie Opie, the Kadina-born choralist who toured Australia, India and the Far-East in the early years of this century, singing to her delighted audiences. She was South Australia's own "Cornish Nightingale".

6) The Bible Christian chapel in Moonta township, erected in the early 1870s. The various Methodist denominations, with their bands and choirs, hymns and Carols, were an important vehicle for the Cornish musical tradition - both at home and in Australia.

Reflecting upon this wealth of local talent, one observer wrote prophetically in 1904 that, "If the history of the three Peninsula towns is written, that chapter having reference to their vocalists, instrumentalists, choral societies, opera companies & C, will form one of the most important and interesting records." *The Christmas Welcome* is certainly an invaluable record of pieces composed, played, sung and — above all — loved by Cornish men and women. Its re-publication here is dedicated to those brave people from Cornwall who, all those years ago, played a central role in the foundation and development of South Australia. Its re-publication also, it is hoped, helps to fill a gap in the documentation of the Cornish Carol tradition.

Philip Payton
Torpoint, Cornwall.

February 1983

Select Bibliography

BOOKS:

Ian Auhl and
Dennis Marfleet,
Australia's Earliest Mining Era: South Australia 1841 — 51,
Rigby, Adelaide, 1975.

D.B. Barton
Essays in Cornish Mining History, Vol. 1, D. Bradford Barton, Truro, 1968.

Geoffrey Blainey,
The Rush That Never Ended: A History of Australian Mining,
Melbourne University Press, Melbourne, 1963.

Inglis Gundry,
Now Carol We, Oxford University Press, 1966.

A.K. Hamilton Jenkin
The Cornish Miner, 1927, republished, David and Charles, Newton Abbot, 1972.

Milton Hand,
Moonta, Wallaroo, Kadina Sketchbook, Rigby, Adelaide, 1974.

Philip Payton
The Cornish Miner in Australia: Cousin Jack Down Under,
Dyllansow Truran, Redruth, 1984.

Philip Payton
Pictorial History of Australia's Little Cornwall, Rigby, Adelaide, 1978.

Kenneth Pelmear
Carols of Cornwall, Dyllansow Truran, Redruth, 1982.

Oswald Pryor,
Australia's Little Cornwall, Rigby, Adelaide, 1962.

Oswald Pryor,
Cornish Pasty: A Selection of Cartoons, Seal Books (Rigby), Adelaide, 1976.

William Sandys,
Christmas Carols Ancient and Modern, 1833

J.H. Thomas et al,
The Christmas Welcome: A Choice Collection of Cornish Carols,
Grummet, Moonta, 1893.

Leonard Truran,
Thomas Merritt: Twelve Cornish Carols, Dyllansow Truran, Redruth, 1982.

John Worden
Strike Sound, Lodenek Press, Padstow, 1971.

NEWSPAPERS AND PERIODICALS:

Australian Christian Commonwealth
Bulletin
Burra Record
People's Weekly
Quiz and the Lantern
Yorke's Peninsula Advertiser

MISCELLANEOUS SOURCES:

South Australian Archives, D5133 (Misc.) *Musical Scores of hymn tunes by James Richards.*

South Australian Archives, PRG 96, *Oswald Pryor Papers.*

Minutes of the Cornish Association of South Australia.

The Christmas Welcome.

A choice collection of

CORNISH CAROLS

Composed by

J. H. THOMAS, W. HOLMAN, JAS RICHARDS, J. COAD, J. HODGE, T. SPARGO AND OTHERS.

Published by

A. GRUMMET

BOOKSELLER AND STATIONER

MOONTA S. AUST.

Printed by C.G.Roder.Leipzig.

7) The original cover of *The Christmas Welcome: A Choice Collection of Cornish Carols*, **as it was published in 1893. Grummet hailed from the Harz Mountains, a mining district in Germany, and the small print on the cover reveals that his collection of Cornish Carols was actually printed in Leipzig! Oswald Pryor wrote that "... Grummet's shop looked like a public library. The long bookshelves seemed to stretch into infinity. Many of the works on view were on theological subjects and sales of them were slow, but they made a good background for the big stock of fancy goods ...** *The Christmas Welcome ...* **sold well".**

Contents

Sound, sound your Instruments of joy.

Arranged by J. H. THOMAS.

Sound, sound your In-strum-ents of joy,—— To tri - - umph

shake —— each string, To tri - - umph shake —— each string.

Let shouts of u - ni - ver - sal joy

Wel - come a new - born

Welcome a new-born King, Wel - come —— a new - - born King.

Welcome a new-born King, Wel - come a —— new-born King.

Welcome a new-born King Welcome a new-born King.

King, —— Welcome a new-born King, Wel - come a new - born King.

2. See, see the glad'ning dawn appears,
   Bright angels deck the morn;
   Behold the great I AM is given.
   The King of glory's born.

3. Surprising scene — stupendous love —
   The Lord of Life descend!
   He left His glorious realms above
   To be the sinner's friend.

4. Let heaven, earth, and sea proclaim
   The wondrous loud abroad,
   And all the universal frame
   Sing praises to our God.

Awake, Arise, Rejoice and Sing.

J. H. THOMAS.

A - wake,___ a - rise,___ re - joice and sing To see the bless - ed morn, To see the blessed morn. A - wake, a - wake lift up your voice, Our Sa - viour Christ is born, Our Sa - - viour Christ is born, Our Sa - - viour Christ is born, Our Christ ___ is born, Our Sa - - viour Christ is born. A - wake, a - wake lift up your voice, Our Sa - - viour Christ is born.

2. O blessed night that brought forth light,
Which made the blind to see,
The day-spring from on high came down,
To cheer and visit thee.

3. Come let us join with angels then,
Our God to glorify,
Peace be on earth, goodwill to men,
Glory be to God on high.

What heav'nly music's this I hear?

Wm HOLMAN.

2. Arise and join the Heav'nly choir,
   In that angelic song;
   Glory to God all pow'r and praise,
   To whom all praise belong.

3. On earth be peace goodwill to man,
   Thus sang the Heav'nly host,
   Let us unite in praise to God,
   The Son and Holy Ghost.

The King of Glory.

JOS. RICHARDS.

The King of glo - ry sent His Son, To make His entrance here on earth, To make His en - trance here on earth. Be - hold the mid - night bright as morn, And heav'n - ly choirs pro - claim His birth. Be - hold the mid - night bright as morn, And heav'nly choirs pro - claim His birth. Be - hold the mid-night bright as morn, Be - hold the mid-night bright as morn, Be - hold the mid-night bright as morn, Be - hold the mid-night bright as morn, Be - hold the mid - night bright as morn, Be - hold the mid - night bright as morn, And heav'n - ly choirs pro - claim His birth. morn,

2. About the young redeemer's hed
What wonders and what glories meet
An unknown star arose and led
The eastern sages to His feet.

3. Let Jews and Greeks blaspheme aloud,
And treat the holy child with scorn;
Our souls adore th' Eternal God
Who condescended to be born.

1

Let all adore Immortal King.

Arranged by J. H. THOMAS.

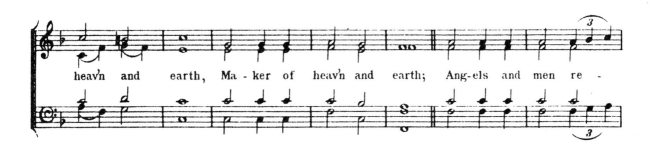

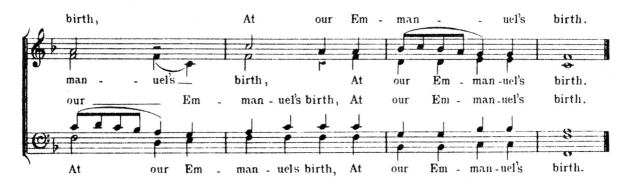

2. A son is born, a child is given,
   That mortals born again,
   Might in the new-made earth or Heaven,
   With God for ever reign.

3. Father, Thy Heavenly voice I own,
   Thy gracious Majesty,
   Through Jesus, Thy beloved Son,
   Thou art well pleased with me.

Hail ever hail, The auspicious morn.

JOS. RICHARDS.

2. Down from celestial climes of day,
   He hastes to tread our ball.
   Glory illumines all the way,
   O crown him Lord of all.

3. Hark! loud hosannas from the song
   The melting air enthrall,
   A Saviour, angels waft along
   And crown him Lord of all.

4. Shepherds to you a herald flies,
   Obey the early call,
   Immanuel in a manger lies,
   Go crown him Lord of all.

Awake with joyful Strains of Mirth.

Wᵐ HOLMAN.

2. In lofty hymns your voices raise,
   His mighty name adore;
   And sound your great Redeemer's praise,
   With shouts of joy therefore.

3. To Thy great name, blest three in one,
   Eternal praise belong;
   Let heavenly angels join the throne,
   And help to sing our song.

Calm on the Listening Ear of Night.

J. H. THOMAS.

2. Celestial choirs from courts above,
Shed sacred glory there;
And angels with their sparkling lyres,
Made music in the air.

3. Glory to God, the sounding skies
Loud with their anthems ring;
Peace to the earth, goodwill to men,
From Heaven's eternal King.

1

The New-born King.

Arranged by J. H. THOMAS,

2. Behold the government He bears
   See what transporting names He wears.
   While all the rays of truth and grace
   Shines o'er the great Emanuel's face.
   Chorus: **We will the Newborn King adore etc.**

3. His wide dominion shall increase,
   And bless the earth with heavenly peace,
   His reign shall over all extend
   Nor shall His Kingdom have an end.
   Chorus: **We will the Newborn King adore etc.**

1

The Prince of Life.

J. COAD.

2. Now may we cease to weep and mourn,
Good news are come from heaven,
For unto us a child is born,
To us a Son is given.

3. He is our Father and our Friend,
The Prince of life and peace,
And since his mercy knows no end,
His praise shall never cease.

Joy to the World, The Lord is come.

Wm HOLMAN.

2. Hark! hark! what news, what joyful news,
   To all the nations round;
   To-day rejoice, a King is born,
   Who is with glory crowned.

3. Behold he comes, glad tidings spread,
   A Saviour full of grace:
   He comes in mercy to restore
   A sinful fallen race.

Mortals awake, why slumber so?

J. H. THOMAS.

2. Arise and go to Bethlehem,
   For in the humble shed,
   You may behold the Son of man
   He's in a manger laid.

3. He came not down in costly robes
   But in a swaddling band.
   He came not down to rich abode
   But dwelt with humble man.

Behold A Lucid Light appears.

Arranged by J. H. THOMAS.

2. While glory unto God they sing,
Glad tidings of great joy they bring,
Good-will and peace to man on earth,
And thus proclaim the Saviour's birth.
Let mortals catch the sacred flame
Till round the world the song shall fly
Which sound the great Redeemer's name,
And glory give to God on high.

1

Arise and Hail the Happy day.

JOHN HODGE.

A - rise and hail___ the hap-py day, A - rise___ and hail the hap-py day. Nor sleep___ the so - lemn hours a - way. Let heav'n - ly_ hosts a - rise___ and sing, Let heav'nly hosts a - rise and sing, Ho - san-na to the New - born King, Ho-san - - na Ho - san-na to the New-born King,Ho-san - - na Ho - san-na to the New-born King,Ho - Ho - san-na to the New - born King;___ Ho - san-na to the New - - born to the New - born King, to the New - born King, Ho-san - na to the New-born King. san-na to the New - born King, King, Ho-san-na to the Newborn King,

2. Peace now resume while gently reigns,
Goodwill and love are given to men;
Thus sang the bright angelic host,
While shepherds weary wand'rers lost.

3. Glory to God who reigns on high,
Proclaim glad tidings through the sky,
Let earth and heaven salute the morn,
On which the Prince of Life was born.

Hark! Hark! What news the Angels bring.

JOS. RICHARDS.

2. This is the day, the blessed morn,
The Saviour of mankind is born;
Born of a maiden, virgin pure,
Born without sin, from guilt secure.

3. If angels sang at Jesus' birth,
Sure we have greater cause for mirth;
For why, because 'twas for our sake
Christ did our human nature take.

4. I am resolved while here I live,
While I'm in duty bound to give
All glory to the Deity,
One God alone, in persons three.

1

While Shepherds watched their flocks by Night.

2. Fear not, they said, for mighty dread
   Had seized their troubled mind,
   Glad tidings of great joy I bring
   To you and all mankind.

3. To you in David's town this day,
   Is born of David's line,
   A Saviour who is Christ the Lord,
   And this shall be a sign.

4. The Heavenly babe you there shall find,
   To human view displayed,
   All meanly wrapt in swathing bands,
   And in a manger laid.

1

What Melody is this I hear.

J.H. THOMAS.

2. Hark how it sounds throughout the sky,
On this auspicious morn,
While hallelujah, angels cry,
The King of Kings is born.

3. Now glory to the new-born Son,
And praised be His name.
All glory to the Three in One,
With loud applause, Amen.

Christians, Awake.

JAS. RICHARDS.

Chri - stians, a - wake, sa - lute the hap - py morn.

Where - on the Sa - viour of man - kind was born, Rise to a -

dore the my - ste - ry of love, Which hosts of an - gels

chant - ed from a - bove; With them the joy - ful

ti - dings first be - gun, Of God in - car - nate and the Vir - gin's Son.

2. Then to the watchful shepherds it was told,
Who heard the angelic herald voice, "Behold,
I bring yougood tidings of a Saviour's birth
To you and all nations upon earth,
This day hath God fulfilled his promised word,
This day is born a Saviour Christ the Lord."

3. He spake and straightway the celestial choir
In hymns of joy, unknown before, conspire;
The praises of redeeming love they sang,
The heaven's whole orb with hallelujahs rang,
God's highest glory was their anthem still,
Peace upon earth, and unto men goodwill.

I

See Seraphic Throngs Descending.

T. SPARGO.

See se - ra - phic throngs___ de - scend - ing Swift to -
ward this ne - ther earth. Hymns___ su - blime___ their way___ at -
tend - ing, Hark they sing the Sa - viour's birth, Hark! they sing the Sa - viour's
birth, Hark they sing the Sa - viour's birth, Heav'n's vast
ar - ches e - cho with ce - les - tial mirth, e - cho with___ ce - les - tial mirth.

2. Round the globe let every creature
Now the Saviour's birth proclaim,
And admire His Heavenly feature,
Then adore His precious name.
All ye nations praise Him in His vast domain.

3. 'Twas for us He left the grandeur
Of the heaven of heavens above,
Well might angels lost in wonder
Celebrate His boundless love.
Let us praise him, may we ne'er ungrateful prove.

Resplendent Beauty.

Arranged by J. H. THOMAS.

With what re-splen-dent beau-ty shone That

long ex-pect-ed morn, That long ex-

pect-ed morn, When Je-sus, Gods In-car-nate

The Lord of life was born,

son, The Lord of life was
The

The Lord of life was born, The Lord of life was

The Lord of life was born, The Lord of

born
Lord of life was born, The Lord of life was born.

born.

2. Thus angels sang at Jesus' birth
While shepherds wond'ring stood—
Goodwill to men, and peace on earth,
And glory be to God.

3. Yet angels usher in the morn,
And they glad tidings bring—
Fear not, to you this day is born,
A Saviour Christ the King.

4. Let saints in Heaven, and men on earth,
Adore Thy worthy name,
And on this day which gave Him birth,
Thy matchless love proclaim.

1

The Promised Child.

THOS. SPARGO.

1. He comes, droop-ing souls, be-hold He comes with heal-ing in His wings, He comes with heal-ing in His wings. The prom-is'd child long since fore-told, Sal-va-tion to the lost He brings, Sal-va-tion to the lost He brings, Sal-va-tion to the lost He brings, Sal-va-tion to the lost He brings, Sal-va-tion to the lost He brings, Sal-va-tion to the lost He brings.

2. Amazing truth th' Eternal One
   Who gave the dayspring to the morn,
   Jehovah's everlasting Son
   This day in Judah's land is born.

3. Gaze ye, astonished Nations, gaze
   Fix on the babe your wondering eyes.
   Hosanna to the infant raise
   And shout your overwhelming Joys.

1

Bright and Joyful.

Wᵐ ANDREW.

1. Bright and joy - ful is the morn, For to
us a child is born, For to us a
child is born. From the high - est realms of heav'n
Un - to us a Son is giv'n, Un - to
us a Son is giv'n,

2. On His shoulder He shall bear
Power and majesty_ and wear
On His vesture and His thigh
Names most awful, names most high.

8. Wonderful in counsel He _
The Incarnate Deity;
Sire of ages ne'er to cease _
King of Kings and Prince of Peace.

4. Come and worship at His feet,
Yield to Christ the homage meet,
From His manger to His throne
Homage due to God alone.

1

Seraphic Throngs.

JOS. GLASSON.

2. Round the globe let every creature
Now the Saviour's birth proclaim.
And admire His Heavenly feature,
Then adore His precious name.
All ye nations, praise Him in His vast domain.

3. 'Twas for us He left the grandeur
Of the heaven of heaven's above,
Well might angels, lost in wonder,
Celebrate His boundless love.
Let us praise Him, may we ne'er ungrateful prove.

High let us swell.

JOS. GLASSON.

2. Good-will to sinful man is shown,
   And peace to man is giv'n,
   For lo! th'incarnate Saviour comes
   With messages from heaven.

3. Justice and Grace with sweet accord
   His rising beams adorn.
   Let heaven and earth in concert join,
   Now such a child is born.

4. Glory to God in highest strains,
   In highest lays be paid,
   His glory by our lips proclaimed,
   And by our lives displayed.

ERRATA.
The second note of the Alto in the second bar of the fifth staves should be an E. The last line is f not p. The second note of the Bass in the last line should be a Minim without a dot, 'wed by two Crotchets F.

Mortals awake.

JOS. GLASSON.

2. In heaven the rapturous song began,
And sweet seraphic fire
Thro' all shining legions rang,
And strung and tuned the lyre.

3. Swift thro' the vast expanse it flew
And loud the echo roll'd,
The theme, the song, the joy was new,
'Twas more than heaven could hold.

4. Hail! Prince of Life, forever hail!
Redeemer, Brother, Friend,
Tho' earth, and time, and life should fail,
Thy praise shall never end.

1

Hark! what mean those holy voices.

JOS. GLASSON.

2. Christ is born, the great annointed,
Heaven and earth His praises sing.
O receive whom God appointed
For your Prophet, Priest, and King.

8. Hasten, mortals, to adore Him,
Learn His name and taste His joy.
Till in Heaven ye sing before Him,
Glory be to God on high.

1